CW00796755

Fire
Burn,
Cauldron
Bubble

BLOOMSBURY EDUCATION
Bloomsbury Publishing Plc
50 Bedford Square, London, WC1B 3DP, UK

BLOOMSBURY, BLOOMSBURY EDUCATION and the Diana logo are
trademarks of Bloomsbury Publishing Plc

First published in Great Britain 2019 by Bloomsbury Publishing Plc
Collection © Paul Cookson, 2020
All poems © the individual poets
Illustrations © Eilidh Muldoon, 2020

A catalogue record for this book is available from the British Library

ISBN: HB: 978-1-4729-5815-0; ePDF: 978-1-4729-5813-6;
ePub: 978-1-4729-5812-9

2 4 6 8 10 9 7 5 3 1

Text design by Clare Mills

Printed and bound by CPI Group (UK) Ltd, Croydon, CR0 4YY

To find out more about our authors and books visit www.bloomsbury.com
and sign up for our newsletters

Fire Burn, Cauldron Bubble

Magical Poems

CHOSEN BY
PAUL COOKSON

BLOOMSBURY EDUCATION
LONDON   OXFORD   NEW YORK   NEW DELHI   SYDNEY

For Andy Camp – one of my oldest,
truest and best friends

CONTENTS

De Magic Poem

I seek de magic poem
De one dat all poets seek
I'm told dat it can ease our sorrows
An good harvest reap
I seek de magic poem
In every language it can speak
It's celebrating our tomorrows
An it never sleeps

I seek de magic poem
I know it's safe
I know it's good
I'm told dat it's full of light
I need it for me neighbourhood

I seek de magic poem
I seek it high
I seek it low
I'm told dat it is out of sight
Another poem told me so

I seek de magic poem
Over de seas
Over de land
I'm at de ever ready
Try and understand

I seek de magic poem
It's in de mind
It's in de skies
I don't want to get heavy but
Dis poem never lies

I seek de magic poem
De one de Pop Stars cannot sing
I'm told it will bring us music
A peace place create
I seek de magic poem
Dat poem keeps me wondering
I'm told it's true, pure an organic
Dis hide an seek is great

BENJAMIN ZEPHANIAH

Whizzo McWizzard's Amazing Creations

Self-cleaning socks for long-distance runners
Self-cooling sandals for steaming-hot summers
Bed socks for dogs and pillows for cats
Spring-loaded exocet-strength cricket bats
Self-inflating life-saving knickers
Pulpits with engines for overworked vicars
All these and more – magic sensations
Whizzo McWizzard's amazing creations

Bananas and oranges – fitted with zips
Healthy and calorie-free fish and chips
Centrally heated warm toilet seats
Non-flavour-fading-non-shrinking-sweet-sweets
A homework computer that fits in the pocket
Football boots with the power of a rocket
Spells and inventions – magic sensations
Whizzo McWizzard's amazing creations

Sprockets and sockets and test tubes that boil
Wires and fires, foil and oil
Springs that go zing and things that uncoil
Hubble and bubble and trial and toil

Jottings and workings with odd calculations
Diagrams labelled with weird notations
Models that move with the strangest rotations
Uttering mutterings, strange incantations

A potion to send your teachers to sleep
A lotion that makes granddad's hair like a sheep
A tablet to take to turn sister blue
A pill to prescribe for a sick cockatoo
A spell you can tell to shut up your brother
A chant to incant to silence your mother
A word that's absurd that freezes up time
A magical pencil to make each poem rhyme
Line after line after line after line
Line after line after line after line
Line after line after line after line
Line after line of his magic sensations
Whizzo McWizzard's amazing creations

PAUL COOKSON

Dreamland

When midnight mists are creeping,
And all the land is sleeping,
Around me tread the mighty dead,
And slowly pass away.
Lo, warriors, saints, and sages,
From out the vanished ages,
With solemn pace and reverend face
Appear and pass away.
The blaze of noonday splendour,
The twilight soft and tender,
May charm the eye: yet they shall die,
Shall die and pass away.
But here, in Dreamland's centre,
No spoiler's hand may enter,
These visions fair, this radiance rare,
Shall never pass away.
I see the shadows falling,
The forms of old recalling;
Around me tread the mighty dead,
And slowly pass away.

LEWIS CARROLL (1832–1898)

Do You Know?

Do you know
That you can go
In the early morning light
When the dew is on the grass
And find the little cobweb tents
The fairies sleep in all the night?
But, alas, you'll find no traces
Of their little fairy faces!

EDITH COLBY BANFIELD (1870-1903)

Over Hill, Over Dale
From *A Midsummer Night's Dream*

Over hill, over dale,
Thorough bush, thorough brier,
Over park, over pale,
Thorough flood, thorough fire,
I do wander every where,
Swifter than the moon's sphere;
And I serve the fairy queen,
To dew her orbs upon the green;
The cowslips tall her pensioners be;
In their gold coats spots you see;
Those be rubies, fairy favours;
In those freckles live their savours;
I must go seek some dew-drops here,
And hang a pearl in every cowslip's ear.

WILLIAM SHAKESPEARE (1564–1616)

I Feel Like I Know Them

I feel like I know them,
those three teenage wizards.

You know who I mean.

It's hard to believe,
that they are not real people.
Real friends.
My friends.

Especially when I dream of them
like I did last night.

In my dream we were at their school together.
It was so real.
So right.

I belonged there completely.

We explored
the shadowy places
that aren't in the books:
endless corridors
dusty stores
libraries and
forgotten classrooms
behind massive creaking doors.

The one who is a bit of a teacher's pet said,
in her kind but uppity way...

'When you read a book
or watch a film
you're only seeing the top of the story,
like an island above the surface of the sea.
To really know a story,
To swim below the surface,
You have to live them in your dreams...
like we are tonight.'

Then we all sat on her four-poster bed,
and talked until dawn
as a storm raged outside.

Please let me be back there
when I close my eyes.

ED BOXALL

I Once Asked a Wizard

I once asked a wizard to make me a sandwich.
Your wish will be granted, he said.
I got what I asked for. He made me a sandwich...
I'm stuck between two bits of bread!

GRAHAM DENTON

19

The Wizard on His Bike

The wizard on his bike
has a song for every spell
and he sings them as he pedals
and he sings them very well.

A spell for high
a spell for low
a spell for shrink
a spell for grow.
A spell for colour
one for plain
a spell for cures
and one for pain.
A spell for wood
a spell for wire.

But **nothing**
for his bike's
flat tyre!

JANEEN BRIAN

Arfle-Barfle-Gloopish-Curd!

Arfle-barfle-gloopish-curd!
Is my favourite magic word.
If I want to stay up late
Or don't want to clear my dinner plate,
I do not cry, I do not yell,
I simply say my super spell.
Mum and Dad will just obey
And will agree that it's OK.
A long lie-in, lots of fries,
Very little exercise
Are all achieved to great success
With the power I possess.
Arfle-barfle-gloopish-curd!
Is not the only magic word
For I know one more of these:
You may have heard it... it's called *pleeeeaaaase!*

PAUL MINTON

Ooshus Magooshus

Ooshus Magooshus
Lives under the stairs
You shouldn't disturb him
You wouldn't dare –
He'll claw at your face
And he'll tear at your hair,
For this is Ooshus
Magooshus's lair.

Ooshus Magooshus
Lives out in the shed
You shouldn't disturb him
He'll have you for dead,
But he comes out at night
(I've heard it said)
To feast on children
In their beds.

Ooshus Magooshus
Lives up in the loft
He likes his bones crunchy
He likes his flesh soft,
He feasted last week
He scoffed and scoffed
And he let out a burp –
You can still smell the waft.

Now Ooshus Magooshus,
He sometimes goes out
He wanders the street
He wanders about
So if you pass a stranger
And you are in doubt
Scream 'OOSHUS MAGOOSHUS!'
With a big, hefty shout!

JOSHUA SEIGAL

The Magic Kitchen Carpet

There's an old and tattered carpet
Upon the kitchen floor
Weather-beaten, moth-eaten
Just behind the door

Colour-drained and food-stained
It's shabby and it's torn
Dead-bare, threadbare
It's weathered and it's worn

On this tattered magic carpet
You can choose your destination
Any wild adventure
And any situation

When the cooking's hot and bubbling
We're somewhere hot and tropical
When wearing Granny's glasses
We're somewhere microscopical

If the ironing is steaming
We're deep in the Sahara
Silly circus clowns
With Mum's lipstick and mascara

If the washer overflows
We're in shark-infested seas
When the freezer door is open
We are in an Arctic breeze

Rockets flying high in space
If Mum does the hoovering
If she rearranges furniture
We are warplanes outmanoeuvring

Assorted jars and bottles means
Experiments and science
And when Dad leaves his wellies there
We're in the land of giants

The ticking of the toaster
Is a robot that is sleeping
An alien attack
When the microwave is beeping

On this tattered magic carpet
You can choose your destination
For nothing's quite as magical
As your imagination

PAUL COOKSON

We Don't Believe

We don't believe in ghosts, Child,
We don't believe in ghosts,
We don't believe in goblins, ghouls,
Or any of the hosts

Of weird creatures you read about,
In comics and fairy tales,
We don't believe in things with fangs,
Sharp claws and pointy tails

Which are said to visit folk asleep,
And steal babies away,
We don't believe in changelings,
Or trolls that force you to obey

Their many evil wishes,
Who can bind you to their will,
We don't believe in leprechauns,
And we don't believe there's a hill

Where lords and ladies dance all night,
And disappear at dawn,
We don't believe in the naiad,
The dryad, or the faun

Who lurk in streams and forest trees,
Or fearsome creatures of the night,
We don't believe in vampires
Who creep inside and bite

You when you are sleeping,
And suck you dry of blood,
We don't believe in children
Living in a wood

Whose feet are turned behind them,
And whose piteous calls
Will slyly lure you to your death.
We don't believe in walls

Covered in moss and lichen,
Concealing magic doors,
We don't believe in fairy folk
Living beneath your floors

Who crawl through your rooms after dark,
Who turn the fresh milk sour,
And we certainly do not believe
In the supernatural power

Of werewolves, zombies, dragons,
Or in houses that are cursed,
There's nothing in the cellar, Child,
So come on!... You go first.

VALERIE BLOOM

Spell to Banish a Pimple

Get back pimple
get back to where you belong

Get back to never-never land
and I hope you stay there long

Get back pimple
get back to where you belong

How dare you take residence
in the middle of my face

I never offered you a place
beside my dimple

Get back pimple
get back to where you belong

Get packing pimple
I banish you to outer space

If only life was that simple

JOHN AGARD

How To Turn Your Teacher Purple!

Heebie Geebie, Hurple Burple
Time To Turn My Teacher... PURPLE!

Simply chant this magic spell.
Soon your teacher looks unwell.
Purple cheeks and purple nose –
purpleness from head to toes.

Feed her beetroot every hour.
See her fill with purple power.
Bloomin' like a purple flower
how she'll screeeeeeeeeeam
when in the shower!!!

Heebie Geebie, Hurple Burple
Time To Turn My Teacher...

PURPLE!

JAMES CARTER

An Example of my Amazing Ability to Make People (Namely my Older Sister) Spontaneously Combust Without Even Touching Them

I pour away her perfume
scribble in her books
dribble on her mobile phone
and give her dirty looks

pull down all her posters
trample on her clothes
then leg it to my bedroom
and hey presto

she explodes

MATT GOODFELLOW

Hey Testo!

Miss Jones (who's quite forgetful)
left the answers in plain sight
then wondered why our entire class
got every question right

M<small>ATT</small> G<small>OODFELLOW</small>

Witch's Wishlist

beetle toe
henbane
first snow
plantain
pig's feet
toad flax
jacklebeet
beeswax
dragon teeth
fairy wing
winter heath
ginseng
wood ears
cypress oil
Job's tears
pennyroyal
burdock root
mustard seed
eye of newt
jimson weed
black mallow
stirring crook
goat sallow
spell book

B.J. LEE

Magic Love Potion

Warning! This will burn flesh,
make your tonsils go numb,
and dissolve all your teeth
right down to the gum,
cause your stomach
to gurgle, your
belly to bloat
after stripping
your vocal chords
clean off your throat.
But if you're determined
to follow this through, gather
these ingredients to power your brew:
love sickness, 2 scoops in a diamond flask
lip kiss prints peeled off of the edge of a glass
7 heartbeats still pulsing, speared on a sharp pin
some twinkle, a throb, and a pang stirred in gin
a stomach with butterflies all caught in flight
a sprinkle of moonbeams collected at night
a lump from a throat, a tinkle of bell
and you have what you wanted,
a potent love spell.

LIZ BROWNLEE

Granny Gristle's Birthday

When Granny Gristle starts to cook,
she waves her wand and whistles.
I help her mix a bubbling brew
of thorny vines and thistles.

She adds a vial of silver beams
collected from the moon,
and two big scoops of powdered slugs.
I get to lick the spoon!

She lets me crack the dragon eggs
and sift the mudwort flour,
then gets the bat's milk from the shelf.
I sniff it. Nice and sour!

We bake the cake and let it cool.
The sweet stench fills the room!
We frost it black and at the top,
I place a tiny broom.

We sprinkle wiggly jelly worms
and spiders on the plate,
and once the decorating's done...
It's time to celebrate!

We sing and dance and have a feast
of cake and toadstool tea.
It isn't every day you turn
four hundred and thirty three!

DIANA MURRAY

Harry Hobgoblin's Superstore

You want a gryphon's feather
Or a spell to change the weather?
A pixilating potion
That helps you fly an ocean?
Some special brew of magic
To supercharge your broomstick?
Witches, wizards, why not pop
Into Harry's one-stop shop?

Tins of powdered dragons' teeth
Bottled beetles, newts.
Freeze-dried cobwebs, cats and rats
Screaming mandrake roots.
Lizard skins stirred widdershins
A giant's big toenail.
Second-hand spells used only once
New ones that can't fail.
Spells to grow some donkey's ears
On the teacher no one likes
Spells to make you good at sums
Spells to find lost bikes.

Spells that grow
And stretch and shrink
Spells that make
Your best friends stink.
Sacks of spells
Stacked on my shelves
Come on in, see for yourselves.
Magic prices, bargains galore
At Harry Hobgoblin's Superstore.

DAVID HARMER

Hoblins and Boglins

Hoblins and Boglins are evil and mean
Rotten and troublesome, ugly, obscene
Horrid and horrible, manic and green
Planting their nightmares into your dream

Hoblins and Boglins are poison and spite
Shouting out lies in your ears late at night
Making up monsters and creatures that bite
Anything nasty to give you a fright

Hoblins and Boglins have souls deepest black
Choosing the darkest of nights to attack
But when the sun shines and dawn starts to crack
They shrivel away and never come back

Until midnight strikes and daylight has gone
The Hoblins and Boglins are creeping out from
The shadows of shadows to wreak havoc on
The innocent daughter and carefree young son

For Hoblins and Boglins are evil and mean
Rotten and troublesome, ugly, obscene
Horrid and horrible, manic and green
They muffle your mouth and silence your scream

Yes Hoblins and Boglins are poison and spite
Embracing the wrong and loathing the right
Hating the daytime, loving the night
They breathe in the dark... and choke in the light

PAUL COOKSON

Proper Wand Care

Don't let your wand wander.
Don't let it out of sight.

Wands gone wild wonder
which wand's wandier, and fight.

Wizardless wands whipping up
magic on their own

start fires, startle sheep and cows
and will likely get you thrown

out of wizard college. So,
keep an eye upon your wand

and if it's looking fidgety
lock it in the fridge
or in a suitcase
or somewhere else that is impervious to magic spells
until it settles down.

A.F. HARROLD

Broomsticks for Sale

Riding on a broomstick
Is the only way to fly.
Feel the wind in your hair
As you race across the sky.
We have a small selection
So buy before they're gone.
We'll even fill the fuel tank
With whatever brooms run on.
They come in many colours
Like red and navy-blue;
Don't forget they can be used
For outdoor sweeping, too.
There is a choice of extras
From a seat to witch's cat
And with every purchase,
We'll give a pointy hat.
You can pay with spells or cackles
Or eyeballs soaked in gin.
Come to our shop in Wandsworth
And take one for a spin.
If broomsticks are too large though
Or you simply want a change,
Why not go for something else?
We have a hairbrush range!

PAUL MINTON

The Not That Willing Worker

I wish I'd stuck to what I knew
and just sat on the mat.
I wish I'd never answered
that advert in *The Daily Cat*.

'Wanted – Willing Worker
for "Offbeat Type" in pointy hat.
Exciting post – with puffs of smoke –
Magic milk – Designer cloak.
Splendid pay – short exam –
must know words like "Zap-shaz-am".'

What wasn't mentioned were the spells,
the cobweb cakes, the test-tube smells.
No reference in the interview
about the meals of spider stew,
but most of all – the awful con –
the fact that I'd be practised on.

These past few weeks I've been a bat,
a frog, but sadly not a cat.
My whiskers now count up to none,
I don't know where my tail has gone.
Tonight, I scurry, without fur,
a cockroach – trying hard to purr.

I wish I'd stuck to what I knew
and just sat on the mat.
I wish I'd never answered
that advert in *The Daily Cat*.

STEWART HENDERSON

What Sort of Pet for a Witch?

Most of the witches you will find
Have a pet of the feline kind
Dark as night – that is that
A pointed hat and a magic cat

A very short-sighted witch that I know
Has a pet and it's a rhino
She only saw its pointed horn
And thought it was a unicorn

Wrinkled, grey and always grumpy
Overweight and skin that's lumpy
Very strange and most preposterous
The witch who had a pet rhinoceros

PAUL COOKSON

Song of the Witches
From *Macbeth*

Double, double toil and trouble;
Fire burn and cauldron bubble.
Fillet of a fenny snake,
In the cauldron boil and bake;
Eye of newt and toe of frog,
Wool of bat and tongue of dog,
Adder's fork and blind-worm's sting,
Lizard's leg and howlet's wing,
For a charm of powerful trouble,
Like a hell-broth boil and bubble.

Double, double toil and trouble;
Fire burn and cauldron bubble.
Cool it with a baboon's blood,
Then the charm is firm and good.

WILLIAM SHAKESPEARE (1564-1616)

Song of the Witches (when their Internet Wasn't Working)

with many thanks to Mr W. Shakespeare

1st Witch:

Double, double, click that bubble
We have got computer trouble
Connection lost – all is tragic
We need new computer magic

2nd Witch:

Wireless charger, tail of mouse
What's the password in this house?
Eye of Apple, USB
Floppy Disk and DVD

Half a text and You Tube clip
Screenshot pic and microchip
Gigabyte, memory stick
Spellcheck button – click click click

Tooth of blue, into the portal
And our spell shall be immortal
Screen's gone fuzzy, keys have stuck
We've run out of magic luck

Computer Witch:

Double double – still got trouble
Your computer's in a muddle
Spells don't work – the answer's plain...

Turn it off – then on again

Your spells won't work,
so let me use my brain...

There, all working now.

Just had to switch it off and on again!

STAN CULLIMORE

The Witch

I have walked a great while over the snow,
And I am not tall nor strong.
My clothes are wet, and my teeth are set,
And the way was hard and long.
I have wandered over the fruitful earth,
But I never came here before.
Oh, lift me over the threshold, and let me in at the door!

The cutting wind is a cruel foe.
I dare not stand in the blast.
My hands are stone, and my voice a groan,
And the worst of death is past.
I am but a little maiden still,
My little white feet are sore.
Oh, lift me over the threshold, and let me in at the door!

Her voice was the voice that women have,
Who plead for their heart's desire.
She came – she came – and the quivering flame
Sunk and died in the fire.
It never was lit again on my hearth
Since I hurried across the floor,
To lift her over the threshold, and let her in at the door.

MARY ELIZABETH COLERIDGE (1861–1907)

The Witches' Cookbook

The Witches' Cookbook, out today,
Is causing quite a stir,
Among the witchy cooks and chefs,
Who all at once concur,
That spellbound recipes like these
Not seen by human eyes
Will make these books fly off the shelves.
Because this cookbook flies!

Delia Dastardly is quoted,
'Love those witchy spells!'
Nigella Nevermore said how
Enchantingly it smells.
Hugh Furnace Whitingtoad wrote,
'Glad the potions are organic.'
And Jamie All-Over declared,
'The puddings are titanic!'

But the witchy supreme challenge
For a chef of magic arts,
Is the Cauldron Blue of cooking
Tangy Tarantula Tarts
They're delicious and they're deadly
As they crawl across the cover.
A combination bound to interest
Any true witch-cooking lover.

The Hairy Wizard Bikers
Stroked their beards and said together
'They are Arachnid heaven.
Pastry's lighter than a feather.'
'But there's quite a risk to eating them.
You really need the knack.
The reason they're so good is
They're a pudding that bites back.'

Mo O'Hara

Witchy Magic

The moon sits high
  The moon shines bright
Beaming menace
  into the night.

The swamp lays still
  The swamp reeks death
Stagnant water
  on its breath.

The mist creeps in
  The mist glows white
As ghosts and ghouls of night
  take flight.

The castle beckons
  The castle waits
Silent gargoyles
  at its gates.

The witches come
  The witches dance
Weaving
  their hypnotic trance.

The night grows cold
      The night is stark
As witchy magic
      stirs the dark.

The spell is cast
      The spell is deep
As village children
      fall asleep.

The morning comes
      The morning brings
A plague of moths
      and crawling things.

The people scream
      The people run
For they know
      the spell has just begun.

The village has crumbled
      The village lays bare
For witchy magic
      has zapped the air.

MARY SERENC

Hatastrophe

I love my pointy witch's hat
The purple velvet gleams
There's just one hitch
For this poor witch
My hat won't fit, it seems

I dare not show my face at night
Without the right headpiece
I'd be a joke
To witching folk
The cackles wouldn't cease

Although I tug and pull the hat
Until my face turns red
There is no way
To make it stay
It won't sit on my head!

Perhaps a strap beneath my chin
Would keep the hat in place
The mirror shrieks
At my squished cheeks
How can I show my face?

I'm really in hot water now
And not the cauldron kind
What can I do?
I'm in a stew
An answer I must find

Then in a flash it comes to me
I'm such a dopey crone
With one quick spell
The hat will swell
My head now bears a cone

DANNIELLE VIERA

The Mad Magician

In a dark and dingy dungeon
The Mad Magician dwells,
Mixing poisonous potions,
Concocting evil spells.

Into his bubbling cauldron
The Mad Magician throws
Handfuls of wriggling maggots,
The eyes of two dead crows,

The bladder of a nanny goat,
The snout of a year-old pig,
An eagle's claw, a vampire's tooth,
Hairs plucked from a judge's wig.

He waves his wicked wizard's wand.
He utters a piercing cry.
From their lairs, deep in the earth,
A thousand demons fly.

In a dark and dingy dungeon
The Mad Magician dwells,
Mixing poisonous potions,
Concocting evil spells.

JOHN FOSTER

Lost Magic

Today I found some lost magic —
a twisty-twirly horn
of a unicorn lying at my feet.
And when I stopped
to pick it up, to hold it
in my fist, I remembered
how once upon a time
you could always find unicorns,
but there are no unicorns now.

You would find them on the shoreline,
flitting in and out of caves in cliffs,
or climbing hills at twilight.
They would lead you through forests,
sometimes hiding behind trees,
and if you lost them or they lost you,
you could always find them again,
but there are no unicorns now.

And it didn't matter
if you followed them all day,
the edge of the world was miles away,
there was nothing to fear.
And none of the unicorns we knew ever
changed into dangerous strangers.
Once upon a time there *were* unicorns
but there are no unicorns now.

BRIAN MOSES

Magic Carpet

Bet you won't believe it
You can take it or leave it
I've got a magic carpet
You just can't beat it
And it only cost a fiver
From a fella in the market
A magic word starts it
You've not seen nothing like it
It weaves like a Wilton
It's got a stylish seat on
It's a supersonic mover
I clean it with the Hoover
It's faster than a broomstick
It can hover like a jump jet
And it only cost a fiver
From a fella in the market
It's got a nuclear pile
and a go-faster pattern
When it rains I never get wet
I just shelter underneath it
The cat won't sit on it
The dog won't fit on it

Best of all it's easy
When you want to park it
And it only cost a fiver
From a fella in the market

ROGER STEVENS

I'm Magic

See this empty top hat?
Use your wand to tap it.
Puff of smoke
and I appear
'cause I'm a magic rabbit.

SUZY LEVINSON

Oh How I Love a Unicorn!

Unicorns are lovely
Unicorns are ace
Oh how I love a unicorn
With their cute pink unicorn face

Unicorns are beautiful
Unicorns are sweet
Oh how I love a unicorn
Especially unicorn meat
It's my favourite thing to eat...

I love unicorn burgers
I love a unicorn steak
I love a unicorn on the cob
And a pasta unicorn bake

I love unicorn sandwiches
Unicorn kidney pies
KFU's too good to be true
Unicorn burger and fries

Uni-pepperoni on my pizza
Unicorn battered with chips
A unicorn korma's warmer
Crispy-coated unicorn dips

Uni-popcorn at the cinema
Or a unicorn Sunday roast
A unicorn kebab is really fab
Unicorn cheese on toast

If you're a vegetarian
And you don't eat unicorn
There's a healthy meat-free option
Just try... uni-quorn

I've got a plan for me and you
Let's have a unicorn barbecue!
Unicorn fillet – fry or grill it
First of all – we have to kill it

And for dessert...

Uni-cornetto!
The best ice cream you've known
A unicorn horn turned upside down
Is... a perfect ice-cream cone

Unicorns are beautiful
Unicorns are sweet
Oh how I love a unicorn
Especially unicorn meat

PAUL COOKSON

Night Soup (a simple recipe)

Take...

A sliver of moon
a nip in the air
a sprinkle of stars
a creak from a stair

Add plenty of dark
the slink of a cat
(with cold green eyes)
a loop from a bat

The patter of rain
the whine of a dog
the taste of a dream
the wisp of a fog

The whoosh of a train
a sniff or a snore
the swoop of an owl
then stop – no more

Then stir it around
and bring to the boil
season with cinnamon
add olive oil

Now let it go cold
and serve quite late
and all
       that is left
              to do
                   is wait...

JAMES CARTER

Crossing the Bounds

Are you wondering about wardrobes now?
Do you feel coats, seeking for snow
and a chill breeze from another land?

Rabbit-holes are not so easily found
in suburbs of asphalt, brick and wood,
but nothing to stop you looking...

Down a bluestone lane of dreams
and nightmares; through a door in a wall;
tick of a clock to change a garden –

Not to mention busy railway platforms.
Let's not go there, we'll get carried away;
or stuffed under the stairs for payback.

Mirrors: how could I forget! Cover them
in sorrow, break them at your peril;
slide into depths with a quicksilver breath,

as you may do with water. Cross boundaries
of lake, stream, river, billabong and creek;
fathom the boundless magic of the endless sea.

What has a spine, a name and a heart,
guiding you safely through margins and portals
to another's imagination and your own?

Keep on turning the pages...   JAZ STUTLEY

Beastly Sounds

We all know...
The hoot of owls
The squeal of bats
The hiss of snakes
The squeak of rats...

We all know...
The squawk of parrots
The whine of dogs
The purr of kittens
The grunt of hogs...

But dragons, ahhh, they sing a different tune...
The rumble of distant thunder
The crescendo of a hundred bells
The roar of a blazing fire
The chant of distant spells.

For they are the most magical of creatures
The kings of sky and sea,
Their beauty and their grandeur
Ring the sweetest tones to me.

MARY SERENC

The Kraken

Below the thunders of the upper deep,
Far, far beneath in the abysmal sea,
His ancient, dreamless, uninvaded sleep
The Kraken sleepeth: faintest sunlights flee
About his shadowy sides; above him swell
Huge sponges of millennial growth and height;
And far away into the sickly light,
From many a wondrous grot and secret cell
Unnumbered and enormous polypi
Winnow with giant fins the slumbering green.
There hath he lain for ages, and will lie
Battening upon huge sea worms in his sleep,
Until the latter fire shall heat the deep;
Then once by man and angels to be seen,
In roaring he shall rise and on the surface die.

ALFRED, LORD TENNYSON (1809–1892)

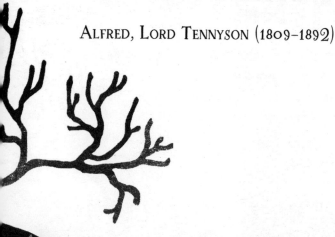

Something Down the Plughole

There's something down the plughole
There's something down the sink
I felt a claw and saw a paw
While at the tap to drink

A weird and eerie creature
Composed of sludge and slime
It crawled up from the sewage pipe
And feeds on grease and grime

Emitting awful odours
It hasn't got a name
The Beastie from the Basin?
The Demon from the Drain?

Who knows if it is friendly
Or if it might attack?
Be careful when you're washing up
In case it wants a snack!

We pushed it with a plunger
We poked it with a knife
But still it stays, won't go away
The lurker in our pipe

We're hearing burps at midnight
We're hearing slurps at dawn
So enter our kitchen at your own risk
Don't say you've not been warned...

NEAL ZETTER

Smellcheck

'I bought a wand from you last week
but when I switch it on
instead of magic sparks it makes
a really wicked pong!

I haven't cast a single spell
that's turned out as it should –
I want to wave goodbye to such
a useless piece of wood!'

'I'm sorry that your wand is casting
such unpleasant smells
I guarantee it won't be lasting –
I can fix your spells!'

'Please tell me quickly what to do –
I really can't endure
the stink of sweaty wombat feet
a single moment more!'

'You really have my sympathy –
that smell will soon be gone
if you just swap the **m** for **p**
by turning "spellcheck" on!'

'Change "s**m**ell" to "s**p**ell" – I see your trick,
for just a single letter
transforms the meaning of a word…
…and now my wand is better!'

HANNAH WHITLEY

Missing: One Ogre

Excuse me, have you see my ogre?
He's greenish and seven foot two.
He's got a sweet swampy aroma
like crocodile-butterscotch stew.

People say that he lurks in the bushes.
My ogre's just terribly shy.
He hates all the pointing and shrieking
when they see him go lumbering by.

He loves to sing songs to the full moon
and swat shiny trains from their tracks.
You should see his sweet-doggy expression
when he's hunting down afternoon snacks.

I thought he was safe in our backyard
but he didn't come in for his nap.
And I think you'll agree when he's cranky
an ogre's more likely to snap.

He's already missed lunch and dinner,
not a munch or a nibble all day.
I'm afraid if I don't find him quickly...
we're going to be late for ballet.

C.L. CLICKARD

In a Stew

I really don't think you should eat me
I'm stringy and gristly and tough
You said it yourself when you saw me
I'm scrawny. I'm 'not fat enough'

That may be the case but
I'M STARVING
I've had worse than you for my lunch
I'll chew on your leg like a drumstick
The bones will be something to crunch

But think of the taste. I'm disgusting!
The flavour of slugs, snails and snot
all mixed in with freshly picked earwax
I'll ruin your best cooking pot

> *Your concern for my diet is touching*
> *but witches don't care what they eat*
> *I once slayed a manky old giant*
> *to make bunion soup from his feet*

But what about girls...
... girls like Gretel?
The ones made of sugar and spice?
You know you should eat her, she's sweeter
and wholesome, and filling and nice

> *Thanks for the tip-off young Hansel*
> *A two-for-one meal deal won't hurt*
> *I'll gobble you up for my main course*
> *Your sister can be the dessert*

JO DEARDEN

The Forest

Somewhere off the path,
beyond the stream,
through the ferns,
across the clearing,
under the oaks,
beneath the leaves,
between the roots,
is a hole.

And in that hole,
if your arm is long enough,
if your nerve is steel enough,
if your belief is clear enough
a fingertip
may brush
the shine of a scale
of the great dragon's hide.

For the great dragon hides
beneath the land,
curled and sleeping,
ancient and dreaming,
rockbound and steaming,
greening the springtime
with fire unfolding,

upward seeping,
through earthworm
and tap-root,
each time she rolls
and breaths out
in her eon-long slumber.

And your pointing finger
touching this secret,
the heartbeat below,
the shine of the scale,
will be renewed –
the tip smoother,
  the print scrambled,
    the nail quicker.

Look close at the fingers
of people you meet
and from time to time
you'll spot the same secret.

Say nothing, but nod,
say nothing, but smile,
say nothing, but know
you're not alone
knowing
what you know.

A.F. HARROLD

Forest Secrets

A jewel-encrusted treasure chest
A thousand years old and a day
Rests beneath an oak tree
Where chattering children play

The silver horn of a unicorn
Its mane of snowy-white
Lies aside a wooded glade
Where badgers play at night

Fairy wings of gossamer
Flash through trees of green
Dancing in the moonlight
Heard but rarely seen

The wonders of the forest
Are buried safe and deep
No one knows their secret
That is yours and mine
To keep.

DEBRA BERTULIS

Scared of the Dark

I'm scared of the dark
I don't like it one bit,
I'm scared of the dark,
There, I've admitted it.

I'm scared of the things
That go bump in the night
I'm scared of the creatures
Outside the light.

I'm scared of the dark,
And what scares me the most,
Is when in the dark
I meet another ghost.

VALERIE BLOOM

Friday 13th

I've dropped my bedside mirror.
You should see the mighty crack!
The cat that crossed my pathway
was most definitely black.
I walked beneath a ladder
on my way to school and back.
I've every right to feel a bit suspicious
that a nasty chain of happenings
has suddenly begun,
that the life spread out before me
will be drained of any fun,
that my luck will not return
until the age of twenty-one.
It's just as well I'm not superstitious!

JENNY ERLANGER

Mathematically,
Telepathically Magical

Think of a number from one to ten
Any one will do
Ready with your number?
Multiply by two...

Once you have this answer...
Simply add on six
With your brand-new total
Here's what you do next...

Halve this number you have got
(And this is the magical mystery)
Subtract the number you started with
And... your answer will be... 3

PAUL COOKSON

A Cold Spell

I can't wait to try some magic.
Promise not to tell.
I'll be witch, and you'll be wizard –
we could cast a spell.
How about some hocus-pocus
on our hazel broom?
Wave the wand – make Monday morning
Friday afternoon!

Freeze the day! I'll make the snow fall –
thick and fast and deep.
We could sledge *uphill* to town –
I'll race you through the street.
Let's throw snowballs and go skating
on the frozen pond.
Make the weekend last forever –
wave that magic wand!

CELIA GENTLES

The Magician with Ambition

The magician with ambition
Was a mystical physician
Who sought the composition
Of a spell of great precision
For all things scientific
His knowledge was prolific
Voltage and transmission, gaseous ignition
Simple recognition of nuclear collision
And specific hieroglyphics
Was wicked and terrific

The wizard of decision
Was a great mathematician
A master statistician
Of addition and division
For all things mathematical
His brain was acrobatical
Fractions and subtractions, factors and reactions
Equation complications, long multiplications
Computations problematical
His mind was telepathical

The solution's constitution
Was brought unto fruition
Magic spells and sorcery
Defying definition
An amazing combination
Of enchanting calculations
A wonderful creation
Beyond imagination
A crazy composition of wish and superstition
Fulfilling the ambition of this magician's vision
And the lotions and potions
Made him such a rich 'un
Thanks to their transmission
On global television

PAUL COOKSON

Out of Luck

I've fetched a cloth, I've made it damp
with silver polish goo.
I'm banking on this little lamp
to make my dreams come true.
I've rubbed and scrubbed. I've really tried.
The smell has made me dizzy.
But nothing's stirred from deep inside.
The genie must be busy.

JENNY ERLANGER

My Pet Dragon

I have a baby dragon
No bigger than my thumb
She lives inside the biscuit tin
And gobbles up the crumbs.

HELEN DINEEN

The Dragon's Curse

Enter darkness. Leave the light.
Here be nightmare. Here be fright.
Here be dragon, flame and flight.
Here be spit-fire. Here be grief.
So curse the bones of unbelief.
Curse the creeping treasure-thief.
Curse much worse the dragon-slayer.
Curse his purse and burse his payer.
Curse these words. Preserve their sayer.
Earth and water, fire and air.
Prepare to meet a creature rare.
Enter, now, if you dare.
Enter now... the dragon's lair!

NICK TOCZEK

The Cool Dragon

Blaze held on to a secret
Buried deep inside her heart,
This secret made her different
And would make her stand apart.
Blaze looked like other dragons
With dark scales as black as night,
A tail of pulsing muscles
Fearsome teeth of gleaming white,
Long claws as sharp as razors
Wings that stretched across the sky,
Eyelids of darkest leather
Black above her emerald eyes.
But Blaze could not breathe fire
Not a single spark or flame,
And if this wasn't enough
To cause any dragon shame,
There was more to her disgrace
It may seem hard to believe,
But when Blaze opened her mouth
It was ice and snow she breathed.
Blaze felt like she was lying
Hiding her truth from her friends

Not using the honesty
On which friendship depends
So she told them her secret
Scared that she'd be called a fool...
'Different is OK,' they said.
'An ice-breathing dragon... cool!'

JO MULARCZYK

How do Dragons Fly?

How do dragons fly?
On wings of skin,
paper-thin,
crackling in the wind.

How do dragons fly?
Exultant,
fearless,
bold,
breathing fire —
their shrieks
split mountains.

How do dragons fly?
With beats,
slashes,
creaks,
in shimmering heat
with glimmering scales.

How do dragons fly?
Over steaming rivers
blackening grass
scorching steeples
leaving a trail of
sparks
and ashes
as they pass.

LIZ BROWNLEE

Dragon's Breath

Scorched earth
Singed bone
Acrid smoke
Brimstone

Molten lava
Soot and ash
Thunderbolt
Lightning flash

Moulding cinders
Long-dead trees
A dragon's breath
Can smell of these

The stench of death
Through and through
Living – breathing
Bar – be – cue

PAUL COOKSON

Potion Problems

I've tried a hundred spells or more
to get myself some fangs.
It's harder than you think to grow
two teeth with overhangs.

Since spells don't work, a potion might –
let's get the cauldron out.
Pour in a lonely seagull's cry
and a sulky pixie's pout...

a witch's cackle...
a wizard's glare...
the midnight creak of a creaky stair...
the putrid stench of a dragon's lair...
and a bolt of lightning's crackle.

There! It's done. *You* try it first.
I know it looks quite weird.
Just have a taste, a tiny sip!

Oh dear.

You've disappeared.

REBECCA M. NEWMAN

A Poem Sawn in Half

When a wizard says 'Abracadabra',
though the tone of that word doesn't grab yer,
you can tell that his spell
hasn't gone very well –
just like this poem that's run out of rhyme
and, disappointingly, lacks a magical ending.

And besides what's a wizard saying 'Abracadabra' for?
That's what magicians say. Wizards say words like
'bassoon' and 'piffle', and 'underarm' and 'galoot',
well all the wizards I know do. And for tea they have
frog-hair cakes and spider jam and lemon ants
and cockroach ham... and see how the rhyme returned...

... all put back together... for a magical ending.

STEWART HENDERSON

I Need a Volunteer

I need a volunteer from the audience
Preferably my little brother
Who has practised this trick with me
All afternoon.
Thank you, sir. Have we ever met before?
Say 'No!' like we rehearsed
A thousand times.
Phew.
Please check inside my top hat
And confirm that there is nothing in it;
That it is empty.
Careful not to turn it upside down
And let all the cards fall out
Of the hidden compartment.
Thank you.

Now, take a card, any card...
That one, you great galoot
The one by my thumb.
And show it to the audience.
They won't suspect a thing.
Now put it back anywhere
You like in the pack.
Where my little finger is.
My LITTLE finger.
Now, I shuffle the pack.
Wait! Come back!
I haven't finished!
And mind the...
Top... hat.
Ladies and gentlemen.
There will now be a short intermission.

PHILIP ARDAGH

From the Wizards and Witches Weekly

Charmers and Harmers – Wandmakers
Official wandmakers since Arthurian times

Choose from our unique selection of handcrafted wands:
The Conjuror – for everyday use
The Enchanter – for the more experienced spellmaster.
The Spellscreecher – echoes your spell in a screech
    while you chant it
The Sesame – a speciality model used for opening
    doors and locks
The Sorcerer – especially useful when preparing potions
The Bewitcher – useful for putting charms on people
The Challenger – used for duelling with demons
The Switcher – designed for transforming humans
    into beasts
The Shapeshifter – a deluxe version of the switcher.

All our wands are carved from the finest oak.
Guaranteed to produce lightning flashes at the
    time of casting.

Contact us at charmersandharmers@wizardry.com

JOHN FOSTER

How to Cast a Spell if you are Vegetarian

Take the eye of a needle
The tongue of a boot
The head of a nail
A car's lonely hoot
Place in a cauldron
Stir it all up
With the swing of a bat
And the lip of a cup
Simmer quite gently
With the tale from a book
Add a finger of fudge
Then take one quick look
But if you are wondering
What this spell will do
Please don't ask me
'Cos I haven't a clue

ROGER STEVENS

The Potions Shop

Come into my cosy shop.
Browse all you like, see what I've got.

Jars and bottles, creams and lotions,
all the best of modern potions.

This green one here does a thing or two
to turn your enemies to goo.

This blue one brings deep sleep, good dreams.
This one nightmares with terrible screams.

Apply this lotion to your feet,
you'll be able to slide down the street.

This purple one on that high shelf
allows you to levitate yourself.

In that cupboard to the right
packets of ingredients wrapped up tight.

Drink this and your way is clear,
you can conquer every fear.

You can order what you need –
we let our customers take the lead.

Special Offer! Three for two.
Loyalty reward points just for you.

Angela Topping

Happy as a Pig in Muck

I once knew a man as sad as can be
Got stung on the bum by a bumble bee
Had to stand for a week or two
Could not sit down on the loo
Wrote away for a miracle cure
Four days later through his door
There came a list and letter
Saying *Do this and get better*
He followed the instructions
Creating this concoction
A most exotic potion
A strange and weird lotion
It was...
Two parts jam, one part cream
Beans, greens, tangerines
All stirred up with a great big stick
Twice a day spread on thick
He spread it on, rubbed it in
Could not believe his luck
The pain had gone, the potion worked
Now he's happy as a pig in muck

Happy as a pig – *Oink! Slurp!*
Happy as a pig in muck

The man knew a boy, name of Lee
Had not smiled since he was three

Never ventured out of doors
A face as long as an ironing board
Sat in a chair – dawn till dusk
A glassy stare – collecting dust
A terminally awful frown
Like a banana upside down
The man said *I know what to do*
It worked for me and it will for you
A most exotic potion
A strange and weird lotion...
Two parts jam, one part cream
Beans, greens, tangerines
All stirred up with a great big stick
Twice a day spread on thick
He spread it on, rubbed it in
Could not believe his luck
The frown had gone, he smiled again
Now he's happy as a pig in muck

Happy as a pig – *Oink! Slurp!*
Happy as a pig in muck

The boy had a dog and called him Spot
Because of all the stripes he'd got
A happier dog you could not find
But nature had been most unkind
A useless tail that would not flinch
It never even moved an inch
Not a wag when he shook a paw

107

Dragging lifeless on the floor
The boy said *I know what to do*
It worked for me and it will for you
A most exotic potion
A strange and weird lotion...
Two parts jam, one part cream
Beans, greens, tangerines
All stirred up with a great big stick
Twice a day spread on thick
He spread it on, rubbed it in
Could not believe his luck
The tail began to wag again
Now he's happy as a pig in muck

Happy as a pig – *Oink! Slurp!*
Happy as a pig in muck

So if you're feeling down or ill
Remember this will make you well
Follow this discovery
To aid your own recovery
A most exotic potion
A strange and weird lotion...

PAUL COOKSON

This is *my* Library

This library is haunted.
If you go in there,
you'll never come out.
There's hidden traps
and secret passages
labyrinthine and deserted
except for... no one knows.

They say even the books
are haunted. Open one
and gilded demon eyes
turn you to stone.
The pages sift over all
by themselves, or turned
by bony inky fingers.

Behind the bookshelves,
in the blackness there,
a thing of darkness lives.
No one's ever seen it.
But it can be heard
leeching the colours
from daylight things.

ANGELA TOPPING

Magic Dog Mabel

My Dog – Magic Mabel
Knows magic you can't beat
She likes to play her tricks
On everyone we meet.

She doesn't need a wand
Doesn't need a spell,
She doesn't need a potion
Or a wishing well.

She just needs some tasty snack
Left out on the table
Then when no one's watching,
It's 'My Dog – Magic Mabel.'

She waves her magic mouth,
The food will disappear
When we wonder where it is
She is nowhere near

She's sitting in the garden
Blameless in the sun
But we all know the food is...
In Mabel's Magic Tum

P.S.
Things also magically appear
From the end that is her rear
But that's a different poem I fear...
Best not go into that right here

STAN CULLIMORE

Somewhere in the Library

Somewhere in the library
there are fierce and friendly beasts.
Dragons, cowardly lions
enjoying midnight feasts.
Somewhere in the library
there are whirlpools and lagoons,
coves and crags and picnics
with pop and macaroons.

Somewhere in the library
there are smugglers' hidden caves,
and voyages and shipwrecks,
where adventures come in waves.
Somewhere in the library
there looms a Gruffalo,
and Twits and Gangsta Grannies
and a wardrobe full of snow...

... Where the White Witch turns the pages,
her icy fingers vexed,
as Voldemort is reading
what happens to him next.
Somewhere in the library
down a whizzing country road –
an amphibian with driving gloves...
the hapless Mr Toad.

There's a Stig, and Railway Children
all present and correct,
whilst underneath the floorboards
the Borrowers collect.
But somewhere in the library
there is someone very wise.
Her title is librarian
which is really a disguise...

... For she's a gatherer of magic
and a confidante of elves,
whose legends she has catalogued
and filed on ship-shape shelves
And she knows a thousand sagas
and ten thousand thousand tales,
she's heard the yarns of hobbits,
and the ocean dreams of whales

So, let me share her mystery,
one secret so sublime –
her special prayer that starts each day... goes...
"Once upon a time..."

STEWART HENDERSON

Spelling Test

At school we had a spelling test – I wore my cloak and hat
I waved my wand and turned the teacher's coat into a bat

It flew all round the classroom and through the open door
And we never saw that coat upon our teacher any more

She told me I was wrong – it's a different kind of spell
Considering she'd lost her coat she took it very well

She giggled then she cackled and found it rather funny
Said I had to buy a new coat – with my pocket money

So when she wasn't looking – another spelling test
I waved my wand again – and the magic did the rest

LES GLOVER

Testing Spelling

A spell to turn someone into a striped horse-like creature... Zebra-cadabra

Spell to turn you into a sideways-walking clawed crustacean... Crab-ra-cadabra

Spell to do your weekly big shop... Asda-cadabra

Spell that takes photographs... Abra-da-camera

A useless mathematical spell... Algebra-cadabra

Spell that makes you hiss and writhe on your belly...
Abra-da-cobra

Spell that makes you sing dramatically in a foreign language... Opera-cadabra

Spell that lights up a very old-fashioned and well-to-do ballroom... Abra-candelabra

A rude underwear spell...
Abracada-bra

A very rude underwear spell...
A-bra-cada-bra

PAUL COOKSON

Unique

A crown well worn
Exquisite form
A single ornate silver thorn

The unique horn
The unique horn
The unique horn of the unicorn

PAUL COOKSON

A Feather From an Angel

Anton's box of treasures held
a silver key and a glassy stone,
a figurine made of polished bone
and a feather from an angel.

The figurine was from Borneo,
the stone from France or Italy,
the silver key was a mystery
but the feather came from an angel.

We might have believed him if he'd said
the feather fell from a bleached white crow
but he always replied, 'It's an angel's, I know,
a feather from an angel.'

We might have believed him if he'd said,
'An albatross let the feather fall,'
But he had no doubt, no doubt at all,
his feather came from an angel.

'I thought I'd dreamt him one night,' he'd say,
'But in the morning I knew he'd been there;
he left a feather on my bedside chair,
a feather from an angel.'

And it seems that all my life I've looked
for that sort of belief that nothing could shift,
something simple yet precious as Anton's gift,
a feather from an angel.

BRIAN MOSES

You will Find Plenty of Poems

You will find plenty of poems
About people being turned into frogs,
Most of them funny,
And some with illustrations to match.
This poem, however, is a different
Kind of magic poem.
This poem can make other poems
Disappear.
See the poem on the opposite page?
No?
Precisely.
Job done.
My magic worked.

PHILIP ARDAGH

About the Author

Paul has worked as a poet for over thirty years, has over sixty titles to his name and has sold well over a million books.

He is Poet In Residence at The National Football Museum, Everton In The Community and lyricist in residence for Sing Together.

Renowned for his lively performances, he visits schools, libraries and festivals all over the world. For more details you can visit his website www.paulcooksonpoet.co.uk or follow him on Twitter @paulcooksonpoet

Alphabetical List of Poems

123

Acknowledgements

'Spell to Banish a Pimple' © John Agard 1996. Reproduced by kind permission of John Agard c/o Caroline Sheldon Literary Agency Ltd; 'I Need a Volunteer' and 'You Will Find Plenty of Poems...' © Philip Ardagh; 'Forest Secrets' © Debra Bertulis; 'We Don't Believe' and 'Scared of the Dark' © Valerie Bloom; 'I Feel Like I Know Them' © Ed Boxall; 'The Wizard on his Bike' © Janeen Brian; 'Magic Love Potion' and 'How Do Dragons Fly?' © Liz Brownlee; 'How to Turn Your Teacher Purple' and 'Night Soup' © James Carter; 'Missing: One Ogre' © C.L. Clickard; Spell of the Witches (When Their Internet Wasn't Working)' and 'Magic Dog Mabel' © Stan Cullimore; 'In A Stew' © Jo Dearden

'I Once Asked A Wizard' © Graham Denton; 'My Pet Dragon' © Helen Dineen; 'Friday 13th' and 'Out Of Luck' © Jenny Erlanger; 'The Mad Magician' and 'Charmers and Harmers' © John Foster. 'The Mad Magician' first published in Four O' Clock Friday (Oxford University Press, 1991, 2019). 'Charmers and Harmers' (John Press, 2019) included by permission of the author; 'A Cold Spell' © Celia Gentles; 'Spelling Test' © Les Glover; 'An Example of My Amazing Ability to Make People (Namely My Older Sister) Spontaneously Combust Without Even Touching Them' and 'Hey Testo!' © Matt Goodfellow; 'Harry Hobgoblin's Superstore' © David Harmer; 'Proper Wand Care' and 'In The Forest' © A.F. Harrold; 'The Not That

Willing Worker', 'A Poem Sawn in Half' and 'Somewhere in the Library' © Stewart Henderson; 'Witch's Wishlist' © B.J. Lee; 'I'm Magic' © Suzy Levinson; 'Arfle-Barfle-Gloopish Curd' and 'Broomsticks for Sale' © Paul Minton; 'Lost Magic' and 'A Feather from an Angel' © Brian Moses; 'Cool Dragon' © Jo Mularczyk; 'Granny Gristle's Birthday' © Diana Murray 'Potion Problems' © Rebecca Newman; 'The Witches' Cookbook' © Mo O'Hara; 'Ooshus Magooshus' © Joshua Seigal; 'Witchy Magic' and 'Beastly Sounds' © Mary Serenc; 'Magic Carpet' and 'How to Cast a Spell if you are Vegetarian' © Roger Stevens; 'Crossing the Bounds' © Jaz Stutley; 'The Dragon's Curse' © Nick Toczek. Previously appeared in Dragons Are Back! (Caboodle Book, 2016). Reproduced with permission of the author; 'The Potions Shop' and 'This is MY Library' © Angela Topping. 'This is MY Library' first appeared in Angela Topping's chapbook Kid's Stuff (Erbacce Press 2011). Reproduced with permission by Angela Topping; 'Hatastrophe' © Dannielle Viera; 'Smellcheck' © Hannah Whitley; 'De Magic Poem' © Benjamin Zephaniah; 'Something Down the Plughole' © Neal Zetter

All efforts have been made to seek permission for copyright material, but in the event of any omissions, the publisher would be pleased to hear from the copyright holders and to amend these acknowledgements in subsequent editions.

For more from some of the brilliant poets featured in this book visit **www.bloomsbury.com**

Welcome to My Crazy Life
9781472972729

Bright Bursts of Colour
9781472963543

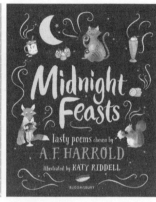

Midnight Feasts
9781472944078

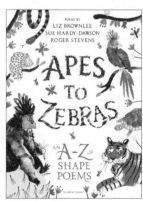

Apes to Zebras
9781472929525

The Book of Not Entirely
Useful Advice
9781526618016

Hot Like Fire
9780747599739